OTTER NONSENSE

BY NORTON JUSTER

ILLUSTRATED BY
MICHAEL WITTE

SCHOLASTIC INC.

New York Toronto London Auckland Sydney

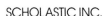

Pen and ink and watercolor were used for the full-color artwork.
The text type is 21-point Bernhard Modern.

ISBN 0-590-62973-5

12 11 10 9 8 7 6 5 4 3 2 1   5 6 7 8 9/9 0/0

Printed in the U.S.A.   08

First Scholastic printing, September 1995

For Emily—Haddock go at the office?
—N. J.

For Sally, Griff, Spence, Drew,
Jasper, General, and Mac
—M.W.

Patriotter

Seal of approval

Oxidentally
on
porpoise

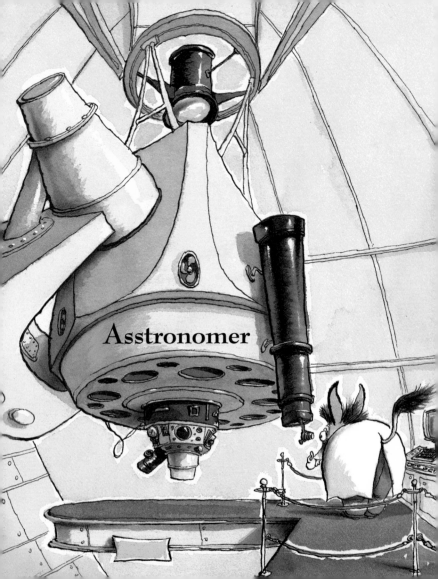

An inchworm jumping
a foot out in the yard

Otter
control

Catastrophe

Pupsicle

Puppets

Soda
pup

Pupcorn

Pupulation explosion

Dog tired

A dandy lion lyin' down

Chipmonk

Wrendition

Wrendezvous

Apetite

Pig out

Bear up

Bear down

Baseball bats

Kangarookie

Striker otter

Fowl ball

Bunting

Ferret out

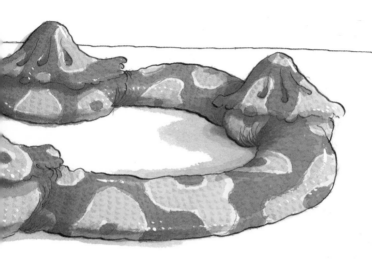

Piethon

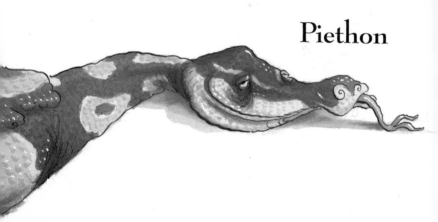

Gopher broke

A hoarse horse horsing around in the horsepital

Larks and bagels

Otter space

Harecut

Marsoupials

A froggy day

in London town

Fast buck

Terrible
cheetah

An aardvark and an even aarder vark taking a vark

A precarious perch

A sole survivor

with a
severe
haddock

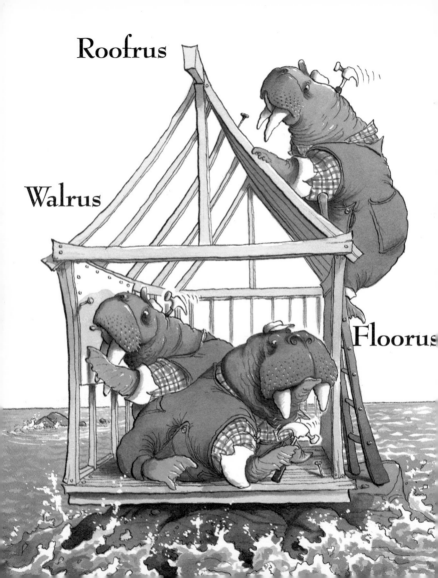

Roofrus

Walrus

Floorus

Plotter

Apeologize

Apelause

Wrenegade

Bisontennial

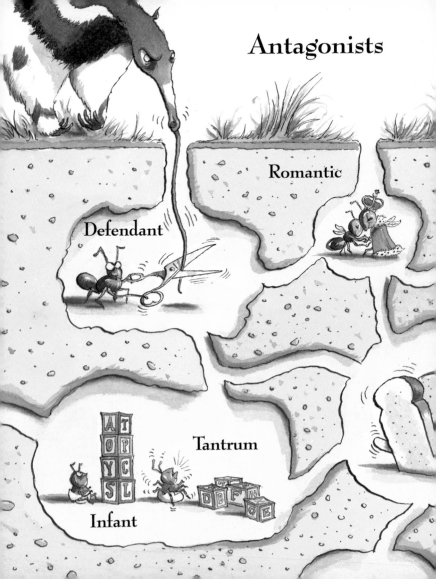

Antenna

Pantry

Vigilant

Dormant

Crocodull

Crocoduel

Ostrich
and
poorcupine

Otter
the
blue

A moose with
a mousetache

A mouse with
a moosetache

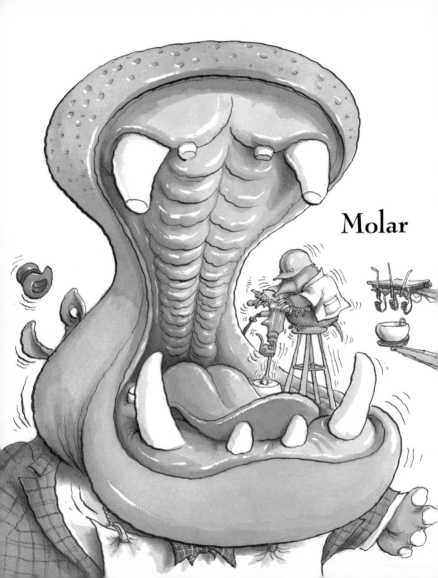

Molar

Hippopottymus

MARATHON

All the gnus that's fit to print

Heron gone

No newts is good newts

We hope you've had some fauna